SNOWFLAKE

For Pauline

by PAUL GALLICO

Snowflake

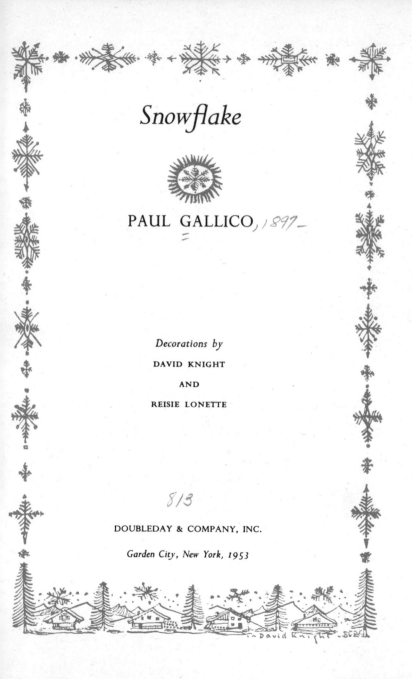

PAUL GALLICO, 1897—

Decorations by
DAVID KNIGHT
AND
REISIE LONETTE

813

DOUBLEDAY & COMPANY, INC.

Garden City, New York, 1953

SNOWFLAKE

THE Snowflake was born on a cold, winter's day in the sky, many miles above the earth.

Her birth took place in the heart of a grey cloud that swept over the land driven by icy winds.

It came about from one moment to the next. At first there was only the swollen cloud moving over the tops of the mountains. Then it began to snow. And where but a second before there had been nothing, now there was Snowflake and all her brothers and sisters falling from the sky.

As gently as lying in a cradle rocked by the wind, drifting downward like a feather, blown this way and that, Snowflake found herself floating in a world she had never known before. Snowflake could not think

5

when it was she had been born, or how. It had seemed almost like waking up from a deep sleep. An instant before she had been nowhere; now she was here, turning, gliding, sailing, falling, down, down.

She thought to herself: "Here I am. But where did I come from? And what was I before? Where have I been? Whither am I going? Who made me and all my brothers and sisters all about me? And why?"

There was no answer to these questions. For the wind in the sky blows without sound, the sky itself is still; the very earth below is hushed when the snow begins to fall.

Looking about her, Snowflake could see hundreds upon hundreds of other flakes tumbling down as far as the eye could reach. And they were silent too.

It was strange, Snowflake thought, to see so many of her brothers and sisters, newborn like herself, and yet to feel so alone.

No sooner had she thought this when she became aware that all about her there was a kind of dear and tender love, the feeling as of some one caring, that filled her through and through with warmth and sweetness.

6

And now Snowflake no longer felt lonely. Secure and happy she gave herself up to the comfort and joy that came with the knowledge that she was loved.

Yet, she was no nearer the secret of her being, or Who it was had created her, or for what purpose, and whence came this deep and comforting affection. She wished she knew so that she could return some of the love she felt flowing from Him to her and which made her feel so content and safe at this moment. Perhaps she would find out more about Him when she came to the end of her journey.

As dawn began to come to the dark world through which Snowflake was tumbling on her long journey to the earth, the sky turned first the blue colour of steel, then grey, then pearl, and looking at herself as she tumbled over and over, fragile and airy as the wind that blew her, Snowflake knew that she was beautiful.

She was made up of pure, shining crystals, like fragments of glass or spun sugar.

She was all stars and arrows, squares and triangles of ice and light, like a church window; she was like a flower with many shining petals; she was like lace and she was like a diamond. But best of all, she was herself and unlike any of her kind. For while there were millions of flakes, each born of the same storm, yet each was different from the other.

Snowflake felt grateful to the One who had given her such beauty and wished she knew how it came about that in an instant He was able to create them all, each one as lovely as a jewel and yet no two of them alike. How great a One must He be to devote such love and patience to perfect one and at the same time so many snowflakes.

It had been bitterly cold high up where she had been born, blown by the freezing wind, but after she had been falling for what seemed like a long time, Snowflake felt that it was growing warmer and the air more still.

She was no longer tossed and tumbled but instead dropped more slowly and softly. And this was a lovely feeling, a gentle, dreamy sinking, always slower and slower as though her long journey might be about to come to an end.

Which indeed it was.

Soon Snowflake could make out objects below her, dark tops of mountains and slopes of snow, forests of tall pine trees and on the side of a hill a village with houses and barns and a church with a round steeple shaped like an onion.

Her brothers and sisters clung to whatever they touched, rocks, branches, rooftops, fences and even the ragged eyebrows of an old man out for an early walk. But Snowflake landed gently with hardly a jar in a field on the mountainside just outside the village, and the journey was over.

A few moments later the storm came to an end and it began to grow light, so that Snowflake, looking eagerly about her, could see where she was.

She lay on the side of a slope overlooking the village and the church with the curious steeple shaped like an onion and below this was a school and a number of little houses with peaked roofs, many with pictures in gay colours painted beneath the eaves and balconies with carved railings running around the second story.

Here and there a yellow light showed in the upper windows and wisps of smoke began to emerge from the chimneys and rise into the still air.

Nearby there was a signpost crowned with a hat of white where some of Snowflake's brothers and sisters had fallen upon it, and the snow came down hiding part of the sign so that all she could read was " . . IESENBERG."

Whatever the name of the village was, Snowflake was glad she had fallen there and not higher on the mountain where there were only dark rocks and a few trees and it looked cold and lonely.

The wind blew the clouds away. The sky became brighter. And then a miracle began to happen.

First the very tip of the snow-capped mountain peak across the valley was touched with delicate rose. Slowly it spread to the next summit and then the next. The sky, the rocks and the trees became tinged with pink; the river winding far below reflected the colour; the snow everywhere was touched with it and soon even the air itself was glowing as though the whole world were but the mirror of a rose petal.

And Snowflake too saw that she was no longer white but bathed like everything else in this soft and beautiful colour.

Then the pink on the mountain tops turned to gold and orange and lemon and the blue shadows on the slopes melted and fled before the light that spilled down like paint from the crests until soon every peak and range within sight gleamed yellow in the morning sun. From somewhere in the distance came the sound of sleighbells. Snowflake thought it was so beautiful it made her want to cry. It was her first sunrise.

Later in the morning, Snowflake had a surprise.

Down the hill on a high wooden sled with steel runners came a little girl with flaxen pigtails, bright blue eyes and red cheeks like two rubber balls.

She was the merriest little girl, who sat bravely upright on her sled wearing a red cap with a tassel and red mittens on her fingers. Her school bag was strapped to her back, she carried her lunch in a paper box, and steered the sled cleverly with her feet, this way and that, sending up great clouds of snow as she whizzed by.

As she passed over, the steel runner cut deeply into Snowflake's heart and hurt her cruelly so that she gave a little cry.

But the child did not hear her. She was quickly gone and only her joyous shouts drifted back in the cold morning air, until she arrived at the school at the bottom of the hill where she stopped her sled at the front door and went inside.

Snowflake found herself wishing that she would come back, for she was so gay and pretty, prettier even, Snowflake thought, than the sunrise.

There were so many things that Snowflake did not understand and wanted to know.

She thought how beautifully she had been greeted by the sunrise soon after she had been born. How simply some One had expressed His love for all the things He had created by painting for them such a glorious picture in the morning sky.

And what a splendid thing to do to make a little girl with yellow pigtails, blue eyes and red cheeks who rode bravely on a sled to school and laughed all the time.

But what was the purpose, and who was meant for whom?

Had Snowflake been born only to be there beneath the steel runner when it came by to speed sled and child along so that they would not be late for school?

Or had the Creator made the girl with her sweet face and silver laugh but to delight the heart of Snowflake? How could one ever know the answers to these problems?

There were so many new and exciting things going on all around that soon Snowflake forgot the questions that were troubling her.

From the barn just below the hill came a peasant wearing a stocking cap with a tassel and smoking a large pipe with a curved stem. He wās leading a grey cow by a rope and had a small black and white dog with rough fur and a wise, friendly face who frisked at his heels. Around the neck of the cow was fastened a square bell that gave forth a gentle and musical "tonkle-tonkle" when she moved.

They passed close to where Snowflake was lying and the grey cow paused for a moment. The peasant cried "Heuh!", the dog barked and made believe to snap at her hooves, the bell tonkled sweetly and Snowflake looked for an instant into her face and saw the great, tender, dreamy eyes filled with patience and kindness and framed by long, graceful lashes.

Snowflake thought: "How soft and beautiful they are." And then she wondered: "What is beauty? I have seen the sky, the mountains, the forest and a village. I have seen the sunrise and a little girl and now the eyes of a grey cow. Each was different and yet they all made me happy. Surely they must have been created by that same unknown One. Could it be that beauty means all things that have come from His hands?"

Now that the storm was over and the day had come, everybody in the village went about his business again. But first one had to shovel a path from one's door to the road, piling up the snow on either side like miniature ranges of mountains.

Then the woodcutter carried out his saw-horse and big, bowed saw and began to cut the logs that lay in his yard into lengths for the stove. His son came to help him and with a glittering axe split some of the pieces into kindling.

Next door the carpenter went to work, planing and hammering on a window frame he was making.

In another house the tinsmith applied his heavy shears and mallet to shining sheets of metal and cut and bent them to the sizes and shapes he desired.

On the farm just above the road, the farmer's wife came out carrying a basket of scraps on each arm to feed the chickens and the pigs. The pigs squealed and crowded to the door of their pen. The chickens shook the snow from their wings and hurried over.

The cold, clear winter's day was filled with the sound of sawing, chopping, hammering and planing, with snuffling and grunting and crowing and clucking.

When the little girl with the red cap and mittens returned that afternoon from school two boys were at her side, each trying to see who could make her laugh the loudest. When they reached the place where Snowflake lay, one of them cried: "Let us make Frieda a snowman!"

No sooner said than done. They rolled together a huge ball for the body and a smaller one for the head. Two bits of charcoal served for the eyes and a piece of wood for the mouth.

"We will give him a long nose, just like Herr Hüschl, the teacher," cried one of the boys, and with that he bent over, scooped up snow in each hand, and began to pack the flakes firmly.

And, alas, Snowflake was amongst them.

How it hurt when she was squeezed until she could hardly breathe. All her beautiful design of which she had been so proud was crushed. When the nose was finished the boy planted it squarely in the middle of the face of the snowman. Then they put a ruler in his hand and said it looked exactly like Herr Hüschl.

The little girl Frieda laughed and laughed and screamed with delight and then she and the boys ran off still laughing and left Snowflake a part of the nose of the snowman who was like Herr Hüschl, the schoolmaster.

At first, Snowflake was sad, for she could not think why this had happened to her.

Always her thoughts came back to why, and what was the purpose of it all? Why had He who had taken such care in the beautiful design He had made for her high up in a cloud let her be squeezed all out of shape to be the nose of a snowman?

Why, indeed, had He made her a snowflake instead of a little girl with blue eyes, flaxen pigtails, red mittens and lunch in a paper bag? What fun it must be to ride downhill on a sled, go to school and have friends.

But soon Snowflake became more cheerful, for everybody who passed the snowman on the hill stopped and either smiled or laughed at the nose which was so exactly like that of the schoolmaster, even to the drop of water hanging from the end of it.

And Snowflake felt comforted. It seemed to be good for people to laugh and be happy. Perhaps it was for this that she had been created and sent to earth. Whenever someone came by she waited eagerly for the laughter to begin.

Then came a day that was not at all like the others had been. To begin with it was quiet and solemn.

The children did not come to the school. No one did any work. Even the barnyard animals seemed to make less noise. Only the bells from the belfry of the church steeple that was shaped like an onion rang out loudly and clearly and with a new kind of authority.

Thereupon Snowflake saw a most wonderful sight. All the people of the village appeared in the square below by the church, dressed up in their best clothes. The women wore long skirts with many petticoats beneath and had their hair done up in braids. All the men were clad in black suits with buttons of silver or horn on the coats and many of them had fine gold or silver watchchains. They wore round black hats with green bands and a *gamsbart* like a small brush sticking up behind.

The children too had on their best ski suits and prettiest frocks, and all the little girls had gay ribbons and bows tied into the straw-coloured plaits of their hair.

Everyone was washed and scrubbed and shined and primped. They all stood in little knots in the square before the church as though they were waiting for something. Snowflake wondered what it could be.

She was soon to find out. For now occurred an even more exciting and wonderful thing.

Down the side of the mountain, on every path and slope, as far as the eye could see, little black dots appeared. They were moving and growing larger and Snowflake saw that there were whole families on sleds, fathers, mothers and children. They were all the people who lived on the farms high up above the village and who were now coasting down to church.

And they too were dressed in their best clothes, for this was Sunday. The dark suits showed up bravely against the white snow. The coloured ribbons of the girls stood out like pennants. Converging from all directions they came whizzing down the hill to land in the square, amidst laughter and greetings. When the last family had arrived, they all went inside the church, leaving the square quite empty.

Then Snowflake heard the music of the organ and the sound of the voices of young and old lifted in song. And as she listened, she felt that her heart was deeply touched, though she did not know why.

Afterwards, when the service was over and the people went home, the sky clouded over and it grew colder. An old gentleman in a black frock coat and carrying a big stick walked by the snowman and paused to look. He had a long nose and angry eyes. He did not laugh as the others had. It was Herr Hüschl, the schoolteacher himself.

No, Herr Hüschl did not laugh at all. Instead he became red in the face and very angry, especially when he compared the nose of the snowman with his own and saw that they were exactly the same even to the drop of water at the end of it.

He gave a cry of rage, raised his stick and began

to beat the snowman until it was broken into pieces and lay scattered on the hillside.

But he was not content with this. He sought out what was left of the head that contained his long nose and with a loud shout of "So!" he ground the offending piece beneath the heel of his muddy boot until there was no longer even the smallest bit of it left to suggest the length or shape of his nose.

Or, until there was very little left of Snowflake, either.

"Help!" she called out. "Won't someone help me?"

But there was no answer and she lay there, broken, dirtied, heavy-hearted and full of pain, listening to Herr Hüschl stumping off still mumbling angrily to himself. And a short while later, it began to snow again.

The new snowstorm lasted all day and all night, and when it was over, Snowflake was buried under many feet of the new fall.

It was quite dark and she could no longer see anything.

But although she could not see, she could still hear, and, listening, she tried to guess the things that were happening above her.

Snowflake knew, for instance, that the peasant must be leading the grey cow home to milk, for she heard her soft moo, and the gentle tonkling of the square bell around her neck.

Thus she strained eagerly for all the well-known sounds that told her that even while she lay buried and forgotten, life in the village was going on. She heard the church clock strike the hours and the bells ring out to come to service. There were the sounds of wood being sawed, nails being hammered and roosters crowing.

Dogs barked, cats meowed. There were footsteps and people hailed one another with "*Gruess Gott!*" as they passed. She even thought that once she heard the laughter of the little girl with the red cap and mittens, and it made her sad with longing for her, for she felt that she might never see her again.

Thus began a new life for Snowflake, and it was not a happy one. Each time there was a fresh storm, or the rain fell and turned the surface to a hard crust of ice, it grew deeper and darker where she lay.

Soon even the sounds barely came through to her, and when they did, they were muffled so that she could hardly make them out. Often it was difficult to tell whether it was the church bells calling to mass, or the hammer of the metal-smith; whether it was the merry cries and shouts of the school children or the gabble of the chickens, whether it was the lowing of the grey cow or the whistle of the railway train running along the river far away in the valley below.

But what made Snowflake the saddest, sadder even than missing the gay children, or the sight of the sunrise and the sunset and the feel of the crisp cool air against her cheek, or losing her beautiful shape and having to lie there in the dark, muddied and soiled, was the thought that she had been abandoned by the One who had created her and whose love had made her feel so happy and secure in the cradle of the wind when first she was born.

 Buried there, Snowflake thought that surely this could not be the end, that she had been born only to see a sunrise, hear a little girl laugh, and become the nose on a snowman.

When she remembered the care with which she had been made and the love she had felt she knew that it could not be so but only perhaps that she had been forgotten. One who could create so many stars in the sky, who could think of a church with a steeple like an onion, who could put together a grey cow with soft eyes and people a whole village, must be very busy.

And so she decided that she would speak to Him and ask Him to help her. And when she had thought this it seemed to her as if He were there, close to her and listening.

She said: "Dear One who made me, have you forgotten me? I am lonely and afraid. Please help me. Take me out of the darkness and let me see the light once more."

And having asked that, she added timidly, "I love you."

As soon as she had said that she no longer felt so lonely but happy and excited instead as though perhaps something wonderful might be about to happen to her.

It began first with a strange drumming that sounded from overhead and seemed to go on endlessly. Snowflake had never before heard anything like it, for it was the noise made by rain when first it falls in the early spring upon the hard crust of the winter's snow.

Yet, somehow, Snowflake had the feeling that whatever was happening above was welcome and might be in answer to her prayer. Her fears were quieted and she listened to the new sound with a sense of comfort and hope.

The drumming softened to a plashing to which was added now a gentle murmuring. The long rains at last had filtered down from above and the waters were moving restlessly beneath the layers of frozen snow and ice that still covered the earth.

Then one day the rain ceased and it began to grow lighter. At first Snowflake could not believe it was true. But the darkness in which she had lived so long turned to deep blue, then emerald green, changing to yellow as though a strong light were shining through a heavy veil.

The next moment, as though by magic, the veil was lifted. Overhead the sun, warm and strong, burned from a cloudless sky. Snowflake was free once again. Her heart gave a great shout:

"The sun! The sun! Dearly beloved sun! How glad I am to see you."

Snowflake was filled with gratitude for her release, and she cried out: "Thank you, thank you!" just in case the One who had heard her prayer and had freed her from her dark prison might be listening.

Then for the first time she looked about her and was filled with renewed surprise and delight.

What a different world it was from the mass of grey and white into which she had been born. Now everything was fresh and green and carpeted with flowers.

True, the high mountain peaks were still capped with white and a few small patches of snow yet lingered on the hillside, but everywhere there was young and tender grass and Snowflake caught a glimpse of small white blossoms like tiny bells on curved green stems.

There were all the old familiar sights, the square schoolhouse, the church, the gaily painted houses of the village, but the trees that once had bent beneath the burden of snow now proudly lifted high their new buds in their arms to show them to the sun.

Since Snowflake had been the first to arrive of the winter's fall upon the mountain, so she had been the last to be uncovered. All about her now there was the rushing, liquid music of running waters.

And because of the great joy and happiness she felt, Snowflake too began to run.

She ran over the smooth grass on to the path and down the hill by the butcher store where the fat sausages hung in rows in the window, past the bakery piled high with new brown loaves, across the market square and by the schoolhouse where at the window she caught a glimpse of the little girl with the red cheeks raising her hand to answer a question put by Herr Hüschl, the teacher.

She ran under a fence and over a gutter; she ran through the farm of the peasant who owned the grey cow, past the barn and around the haystack, over the yellow feet of a white hen engaged in pulling a worm from the ground, and under a black cat who leaped into the air and shook his paw in the most amusing manner.

She ran past a boy bouncing a rubber ball and another spinning a top; she ran over a meadow that was full of yellow primroses and across a field where a farmer with his two big horses was cutting a deep furrow with his plough. She ran through a quiet wood and awakened the first violet beneath its broad green leaf. She ran. . . .

And as she did so she noticed for the first time that something strange had happened to her. She was different from what she had been before.

A wondrous and exciting change had taken place. Snowflake was no longer a lace-like creature of stars and crosses, triangles and squares all woven into one pattern that was all her own. Now she was round and as pure as the morning light, crystal clear and like a tiny silver mirror she was able to catch and give back every colour in the world about her.

One moment she took on the emerald green of a frog sitting on a piece of moss, and the next she flashed crimson as for an instant she reflected the gill of a swift-darting brook trout.

She copied the deep purple of a crocus growing near the bank, changed to the yellow of the first buttercups, and a minute later took on the sombre brown of an old oak tree.

Thereafter she mirrored the pale pink of the cherry blossom, then the tint of orange filched from the breast of a robin as he flew by, and the light blue of the spring sky. The grey of a rock, the black of a crow's glossy wing, the dapple of a young calf, all were hers.

Snowflake could not stop running once she had started down the hill. She did not know that she had begun a long journey, that she must run ever-more and that not until the end of her days would she ever again be still.

All about her were her brothers and sisters who had tumbled out of the sky with her the day she was born and who too had changed from white snow to crystal-clear water, and they had joined Snow-flake on her voyage.

But now it was more than merely running over the hill. It was a headlong dash, a leaping over beds of smooth stones and pebbles, a flinging of oneself down, down, downwards with a sweet sense of freedom, of making music as one went, a splashing, murmuring, gurgling, rushing that lifted Snowflake's heart and made her feel happier than she ever had been before.

How thrilling life had become, throwing oneself over the edge of a little falls to tumble unharmed into a frothing pool below, swirling around jagged rocks or moving in stately fashion through a deep dark pool where a willow dipped its young shoots.

What sights there were to be seen as Snowflake went rushing down the side of the mountain some-times in bright sunshine and at others through the dark of pine forests which the sun had not yet warmed so that at times she ran between banks of snow still unmelted and saw brothers and sisters of hers that had not yet been changed and must still wait.

To them she called back gaily: "Come . . . come . . . Do not stay there so cold and unhappy. It is spring. There is so much to be seen and so much to be done. Follow me . . . follow me away, dear brothers and sisters!"

But there was not even time to look back to see if they were coming, so fast was she leaping and dashing over rock and rill until she came to the bottom of the mountain where flowed a broader but more placid stream winding between low green banks. Alongside it ran the railway with every so often a train passing by filled with people.

Snowflake saw that this was the distant valley and the tiny toy railway that she used to see from high on top of the mountain where she had lived when she was a child. She felt quite grown up when she entered the dark-green, glassy waters of the stream.

With a froth and a swirl, the mountain brook entered the valley stream and Snowflake with it, and at once she began to move off with the strong, deep, steady current of the water.

There was yet time for Snowflake to look behind her for one last glimpse of whence she had come. High up on the green mountain she saw the houses of the village clinging to the side of the hill. She could even make out the white schoolhouse with the dark shingled roof, and the grey stone church with the steeple shaped like an onion, only now it was *their* turn to look tiny like the toys of children.

To her surprise she saw that the peak of the mountain that rose high above the village was still white and covered with snow.

And she thought how strange that so many of her brothers and sisters had been fated to remain behind while she had been chosen to change into what she was and go off to see the world. And she wondered why. Then she thought of the One who had made her and who must love her more than all the others, since He was so kind to her. Yes, that must be it.

Not long after, Snowflake had an adventure.

She was aware that she had been moving faster and faster for a while, almost as quickly as the railway cars pulled by the engine with a great noise and clatter along the tracks nearby.

The banks of the stream narrowed and Snowflake could hear a far-away rushing and roaring, but quite different from the noise made by the train and somehow she knew that it would have to do with her.

Even the surface of the water of which she was a part now became uneasy, forming into little swirls and whirlpools at times and at others hurling itself forward like a wall of molten glass.

Faster and faster it went. Louder and louder grew the roaring. It seemed as though all about Snowflake arose a cry: "Look out, everyone, here we go!"

And then with a rumble like thunder, over she went, into a black abyss, and the next moment, gasping, choking, drowning, she was whipped to a white froth, crushed, torn and churned by the great wooden wheel of a mill.

Splash! she went on to the broad wooden blade of the wheel, blinded and crushed by the weight of the water thundering down upon her from above.

Her ears were made deaf by the turmoil of the falls, the rumbling of the huge wheel, the creakings and the groanings that came from all its parts as it trembled beneath the force of the water and slowly turned and the harsh noise of the grindstones clashing within.

She could not even cry for help so shaken was she by what was happening to her. She was sure that she had reached the end of her days and was about to perish.

Then the wheel sank beneath the weight of the water and Snowflake found herself freed again. She fell into a turmoil of foaming white froth and was swept away. A moment later she was again a part of the calm stream, gliding along past newly budded trees.

But back at the mill, behind her, she heard a woman saying to the miller: "What beautiful white flour! I will buy a kilo and bake bread for my husband and my children."

The mountains on either side of the valley became smaller and less rugged. The stream met another coming from the west, and running beneath the grey arch of a stone bridge that had been built by the legions of Caesar, the two were joined together to make a small river that moved along at a more stately pace. With them went Snowflake.

She was still shaken and trembling because of what had happened to her at the mill wondering what new perils lay before her and whether she would have the courage and the strength to meet them. She even considered whether it might perhaps not be better to be lying quietly and safely in the peaceful snowfields of the mountain peaks that were now all but vanished in the distance.

It was the being alone that was the most discouraging. True, she was surrounded on all sides by others like herself, but this, she found, made for one's being even lonelier, for they were all busy with themselves and nowhere did she hear a friendly voice nor did anyone seem to care about her or what happened to her.

Until one bright warm day, all this was changed.

The river had become both wider and deeper. Sometimes Snowflake was in the cool green depths admiring the movements of the long, swift pike, the eager perch, the lazy, graceful trout. At others she was swept along the surface past trees, houses and villages that were becoming more like towns.

It was during one of the latter that she heard a voice beside her say:

"Hello. You're a snowflake, aren't you?"

"Yes," replied Snowflake.

"I think you're beautiful," said the voice.

Snowflake was astonished and pleased. It was the first time that anyone had noticed her or spoken to her directly.

"Do you really?" she said. "That is very kind. But who are you?"—and she looked all about her to see who it could have been who had spoken.

"Here I am," said the voice right beside her. "I am a Raindrop."

Snowflake looked then in the direction whence the voice came, and saw him. And sure enough it was a Raindrop.

He was large, strong and handsome in a pear-shaped way, and Snowflake thought that he too was beautiful as he floated along next to her, sparkling in the sunshine and reflecting the colour of the sky.

How good it was to have someone to talk to! She asked: "Where did you come from?"

"Out of the sky, like yourself," Raindrop replied. "I was born in a cloud many months ago, but did not fall until only a few days ago. I followed you down the mountain. But I didn't dare speak to you before."

"No?" Snowflake asked. "Why?"

"Because you are so beautiful."

Snowflake thought this a strange reason for not speaking to someone, but not wishing to be impolite, did not say so. And besides it pleased her to have him say it again.

Now Raindrop spoke more shyly. "I say," he said, "but you were brave in that mill-race. I was sure we were done for. But I was watching you and it gave me courage."

A most delicious feeling stole over Snowflake. Someone had thought her brave when she was sure she had been more frightened than anyone. . . .

Snowflake said to Raindrop: "Tell me about your being born. What was it like?"

"It happened over Iceland, I think," Raindrop replied. "It seemed as though I woke up one morning, and there I was part of a cloud that contained many other raindrops like myself."

He continued: "We travelled for a long time pulled or pushed by the wind, here, there and everywhere. When we looked down from the sky, all we could see was snow and ice. Sometimes we saw heavy clouds beneath us and the snowflakes falling, but we remained high up because it was not yet our time."

"Why was it not yet your time?" Snowflake asked.

"I do not know," replied Raindrop. "Who can say? Then one day we met a current of warm air and we began to fall."

Snowflake remembered her own descent. And this led her once more to remember Him. She asked: "Who made us? Why did we fall? Why were we sent here? Did you ever feel as though some One loved you very much and was watching over you?"

Raindrop replied: "I cannot tell. I only know that since I first saw you I have not been able to think of anything else, only you. Will you come with me, Snowflake?"

Again, the warm, happy feeling came over Snowflake. It was good to have someone near her who cared about her.

She replied to Raindrop: "How kind you are! Will you wait? I cannot give you my answer yet."

"I will wait," Raindrop replied.

The land was changing all about them. The high jagged mountains had disappeared and in their place were low, rolling hills and meadows covered with flowers. Towns along the banks became more frequent. Sometimes the river flowed straight as an arrow, others it would wind and twist like a serpent. And no one could tell what lay ahead.

Yet all of the time Snowflake felt secure and comforted because Raindrop was near her and never strayed from her side. One day, Snowflake felt that she was certain.

She cried: "Raindrop . . ."

"Yes, dear Snowflake?"

"You have been patient and good to me. I will give you your answer. Yes, I will come with you if you still want me."

For a time then, Snowflake and Raindrop glided along silently side by side down the blue and golden path made by the reflection of the setting sun in the sky.

"Dear Snowflake," Raindrop said.

"Dear Raindrop," Snowflake replied shyly.

Then they united, one with the other.

And thereafter they continued to flow with the river and were no longer two but one.

She was Raindrop, and Raindrop was Snowflake. They were still in many ways themselves, but each was now a part of the other.

So perfectly did they blend that it seemed as though thereafter they thought with but one mind, spoke with one voice and lived with but one soul.

Each seemed to understand what the other wished or felt before it was even said. Each gave of his or her strength. United, they felt secure against anything that might befall them.

Snowflake remembered all the good things that had happened to her since she was born, the cradle of the wind, the sunrise, the little girl, the release from the snow prison, the run down the hill. . . . She felt she had never been as happy as she was now.

Some time later, Snowflake cried out: "Raindrop! Where are we? What has become of our river?"

The banks of the river past which they had been gliding for so long were no longer there. Instead they seemed to be a part of a large, smooth, blue body of water. The land on both sides was far distant and low.

"Of course," said Raindrop, who knew many things. "We have flowed into a lake. How splendid! Now we may rest for a while."

"I am glad," Snowdrop said. "I am tired after so much running. It will be good just to remain here together quietly in the sunshine."

"And when it is too warm," Raindrop said, "it will be cool and sweet at the bottom, for the lake is very deep."

"How happy I am to be here, dear Raindrop!"

But already a shadow was approaching on the surface, accompanied by a strange clicking noise.

"Oh!" Snowflake cried. "What can it be?"

Raindrop soothed Snowflake's fears at once. "It is only a man in a rowing boat," he told her. "He is going to pass over us. He expects us to hold him up."

Snowflake said: "Once when I lived up on the mountain I was run over by a little girl with a sled, and it hurt."

"This is different," Raindrop promised. "You will hardly feel anything. Besides, don't forget, there are two of us now. We are together."

The boat, rowed by a fisherman wearing a crumpled hat, passed over them, and Snowflake felt only a sense of sweetness and of power as she helped to hold him up, and then in the form of a little wave, slapped gently against the side of the boat.

"Let's do it again," she cried, "that was fun!"

After that, she and Raindrop held up many kinds of boats, graceful sailing dinghies that glided by without a sound, long, slender barges, noisy, roaring motorboats, and once even a large white steamboat that swept them up with its paddle wheel and whirled them over, hissing with steam and clanking loudly. But because she was with Raindrop, Snowflake was not afraid and even enjoyed the excitement.

Thus Snowflake and Raindrop remained in the lake for many days and weeks, resting, drifting idly and learning many things about the world in which they were living.

Sometimes they floated close to the shore amidst green lily pads crowned with yellow and white blossoms, where the water birds rustled in the reeds and frogs and turtles sunned themselves on old logs. The voices of the frogs changed from their spring to their summer songs and the turtles stared with sleepy eyes.

Other times they passed beautiful villas near the edge of the lake, villages, and even a small town with a railway station and a steamboat pier from which the white steamer with the paddle wheels departed.

The steamer had a huge red flag with a white cross on it of which she was very proud. Snowflake and Raindrop became good friends with her, played with her often, and helped to hold her up. They always knew when she was coming for she would give a long tuneful blast on her whistle as she sailed up the lake.

Many people came to live by the edge of the lake, for it was the time of summer holidays.

They went into the water to swim and Snowflake and Raindrop laughed to see how awkward they were at it, snorting, splashing and coughing as they churned over the surface, compared with the silvery fishes who had only to think where they wished to go and with a single wave of their fins and a flip of their tails they were there.

On the strand where the blue lake lapped against a beach of yellow sand, children waded, their skirts and trousers rolled up to their thighs, and Snowflake loved to play about their fat little legs and hear them scream with joy as the wavelets spanked against their brown skins.

On moonlit nights, lovers came out in skiffs and

allowed their oars to drift idly while they sat with their heads together and let their hands trail in the cool water. Then Snowflake and Raindrop would pass by and caress their fingers.

At such times, Snowflake would ask: "Do you still love me as much as when you first saw me?" And Raindrop would reply:

"But of course I do. What a silly question to ask."

Snowflake would smile contentedly at his answer.

Time passed. There came a day when Raindrop said to Snowflake: "Have you noticed anything?"

"It seems as though we are moving again," she replied.

"Yes. We have come to the end of the lake."

It was true. They had left the place where they had entered far behind, so far that they could not even see it any more, so far indeed that not even a glimpse of the distant snow-capped mountains was any longer to be had.

They were close to the banks of quite a large city with many churches, towers, stone buildings and green parks. Slowly but surely they felt themselves being swept by.

They came to an opening in the shore where they passed beneath a bridge and thence into a kind of canal, the sides of which were lined with stone and tall gabled houses. They were moving more quickly now. Then the canal led to a broad river into which they were drawn, and soon the city was left behind.

The long, happy rest was over. The journey had begun again.

The river in which Snowflake and Raindrop now found themselves was a broader and more stately one than the first they had encountered after their breathless run down the mountain.

Its pace was more slow, its bends wide and graceful, and there was time to look about to see everything as they moved along with the current.

It was a much busier river too, and because it was both deep and wide, there were almost as many boats on it as there had been on the lake, from small canvas canoes with double paddles, worked by brown young men bare to the waist, to the long barges flying the gay pennants of the family wash from the stern, and the busy tugs and steamers with coloured flags nailed fore and aft, and black smoke rising straight up from their smokestacks.

Snowflake was used to boats now, and she and Raindrop made it a point to pass beneath them whenever one came near so as to help to hold them up. They liked best to go beneath the barges, for there always seemed to be cheerful accordion and harmonica music coming from them, and everyone aboard appeared to be living a happy and carefree life, including the dogs and children.

One day, not long after they had left the lake and were floating with the river through a green valley whose slopes were tiered with vines on which hung great clusters of white grapes, Raindrop said:

"Snowflake, dear, whose are all those many little voices I seem to hear all about us, and to whom you speak from time to time?"

Snowflake smiled shyly and said gently: "I was wondering when you would notice. Those are our children, dear Raindrop."

Raindrop was greatly pleased, but could only say: "Well . . ." and then once more, "Well, well! How many of them are there?"

Snowflake counted them again to make certain and then said with pride: "Four."

"Four! That is a fine number. What are their names?"

Snowflake thought first to get them right and in the proper order before she replied: "They are called Snowdrop, Rainflake, Snowcrystal and Raindrop-Minor."

Raindrop said: "Well, well, well, well." And then added, "I think those are very nice names."

Raindrop did not appear to pay much attention to the children after that, though secretly he was very proud of how handsome they were and would watch out of the corner of his eye as they swirled and played about Snowflake or went for rides on tiny air bubbles on the surface of the river. Once in a while he would speak with them and try to answer their questions.

But Snowflake seemed from then on to be busy from morning until night, keeping them clean, brushing away bits of oil or soot or dust that came flying through the air from the smokestacks of the steamers and got on to their faces, watching to see that they did not stray too far from her side, holding on to their hands when they passed beneath a boat and teaching them all she had learned about floating down a big river.

Still there was time left to enjoy the points of interest and note the many fine and exciting things to be seen, such as cars whizzing by on the white ribbon of road that ran along the bank, railway trains on both sides of the river, gay cafés and restaurants with tables on terraces beneath coloured umbrellas and the ruins of many old castles crowning the hilltops, their bare walls standing out darkly and full of mystery against the evening sky.

Thus one day seemed to pass like another in contentment and interest and things of even greater moment lay ahead, for in the far distance they could catch a glimpse of the towers and steeples of a city much larger than they had ever seen before, and the twin spires of a great church rising from the river haze.

They happened to be travelling close to the left bank at that time and suddenly before they were aware of it a narrow opening appeared in it with a kind of floor of stone paving that was slanted sharply downhill for a short distance so that they were unexpectedly swept into it with a rush.

Gone was the broad, placid river flowing between the lofty hills; gone the slow, gentle pace that allowed one to think and dream as one floated along.

They were caught in a narrow man-made canal of smooth granite blocks. And they were dashing along faster and faster all the time.

Raindrop looked grave. "I do not like this at all," he said.

"No," Raindrop repeated, "I do not care for this in the least. Had I thought that something like this might occur I should have kept us all well out in the middle of the river."

Snowflake now became alarmed herself, for she had never seen Raindrop so serious or disturbed. She cried:

"What is happening? Are we in danger?" And quickly called to Snowdrop, Rainflake, Snowcrystal and Raindrop-Minor to come to her at once, give her their hands and stay close to her side.

Raindrop looked even graver. The sides of the canal were steeper now so that they could no longer see much of the sky above them. And faster, always faster was the pace at which they were being swept along.

"I am not sure," Raindrop replied, "but keep the children together and stay close to me. Whatever; we must not be separated now."

The next moment, the canal became roofed over, the sky vanished, and with a gurgling roar and sucking sound they plunged into the mouth of a dark tunnel.

It was fearful to be hurled along through the pitch black, unable to see or know where they were going.

The entrance to the tunnel fell further and further away behind them. As they gazed back in despair, first it looked like this—O, then smaller, like this —O, then smaller still, like this—o, and then, alas, only like this—o.

And thereafter, not so much as a single gleam or ray of light entered to relieve the gloom through which they were plunging.

Snowflake was frightened as she had never been before, but for the sake of the children she pretended she was not and asked Raindrop calmly: "Where do you think we are?"

"Underneath the city, the huge one we saw in the distance," he replied, "or if not, we will be soon. We may have luck and escape with nothing worse than to be drawn in a bath, or used to wash dishes. But there are hundreds of things which can happen to us." He dropped his voice to a whisper: "If only we do not meet our greatest enemy . . ."

Snowflake said softly: "Who is our greatest enemy, Raindrop? Whisper it to me. I don't want the children to see how frightened I am."

"Shhh," Raindrop replied. "Have courage. Perhaps it will never happen. Remember, I am with you."

But the tunnel through which they were dashing grew more chill and narrow all the time. It had many branches that opened to left or right. Fortune, good or bad they knew not which, swept them this way or that but always onwards.

The speed increased. The space through which they were rushing became always smaller. It changed from stone to brick and then from brick to iron as they entered the mains pipe beneath the city.

Faster, faster, faster! Some mighty power had them in its grip. Then without warning they felt themselves being snatched upwards. Sounds reached them, the clanging of bells, shouts, the breaking of glass, a thumping and a roaring . . .

Raindrop cried: "Courage, Snowflake! It *is* our most bitter foe."

"Who is it?" Snowflake gasped.

Raindrop then pronounced the terrible word: "Fire!"

There was so little time left now even to be afraid.

Above, the powerful pumps were drawing them up from the depths at blinding speed. Snowflake felt helpless and lost. The children were snatched from her though they still managed to cling to Raindrop.

As the pipe narrowed and the pressure increased she thought she would be crushed to death. But worse was yet to follow. Caught in a grip like that of a giant she was forced into a long, flexible tube at such speed that she could barely cling to her senses. Nothing so painful or terrible had ever happened to her before. Snowflake threw one last, despairing look at Raindrop, for she was certain she could bear no more.

Then with a great spurt and a cry of agony, she burst into the open and for an instant gazed upon an awful scene.

There was a house in a crowded city street before her. Black smoke and yellow flames were pouring from the roof and windows. Orange tongues of fire were licking upwards.

She heard Raindrop call to her: "Give all your strength, all your heart and soul, Snowflake! We must win!"

Then, with the powerful stream of water shot from the brass nozzle of the hose held by the firemen, she was hurled straight for the centre of the fiery furnace.

At once she was enveloped by flames and fearful heat while from all about her came a terrifying crackling and roaring, a splintering and tearing, a thundering and a crashing.

Stifling black smoke filled the air. The heart of the fire glowed red and evil. Bright blades of yellow flames leaped like sword strokes to destroy all in their path. Water was turned to steam and with it the blaze hissed its defiance.

Gasping for life, all but seared by the blast from the raging furnace, Snowflake was near to giving way to despair and defeat. Who could prevail against an enemy so savage and so strong? Another second and she felt she must shrivel, boil and turn to vapour. And yet she did not surrender.

She recalled what Raindrop had said: "Give all your strength, all your heart and soul. We must win!"

And in that moment she thought of the One from whom her heart and soul had come, and she cried out to him: "Help us. Remember, when I was a child you loved me. . . . If you must, take me, but spare Raindrop and my children."

Then having done so, she bent all her will and tried with might and main to fight against the enemy.

In that instant, Snowflake and all those who were rallied beside her in the fight against the red destroyer struck at the glowing heart of the living flame and vanquished it.

There was the sound of drenching, frothing and hissing. With a mortal shriek and emitting clouds of steam and smoke, the wounded fire made a final effort to survive. One last darting orange spear of flame was cast to try to snatch victory from defeat. It was drowned beneath the tons of water that followed upon Snowflake's gallant and victorious assault. The fire fell back dying.

At a window which a moment before had been all but engulfed by flames, there appeared a fireman carrying in his arms an infant, sleeping and unharmed.

A great cheer went up from the crowds in the street below as he handed him over to a companion who carefully carried him still sleeping down the ladder to safety and his mother who awaited him there.

This was the last that Snowflake saw, for just then her mind swam, her eyes became clouded and of the hour of her greatest triumph she could remember no more.

When, much later, she returned to her senses, it was to find herself trickling down the side of the blackened building, all soiled and dirtied from the soot and cinders.

She was so weak she could hardly stir and once she thought she must meet her end there on the side of the house from the heat still rising from the glowing embers beneath.

At that instant, with a surge of joy, Snowflake saw Raindrop and the children flowing down a charred beam nearby and forgetting about herself in the happiness of finding them she felt her strength return.

She called to them; they saw her; their paths down the side of the ruined building converged and soon they were united again. And in the immediate excitement of the moment, Snowflake was only just aware that Raindrop was no longer the person he had been. He appeared to be changed by the ordeal through which they had passed.

Snowflake now swiftly counted her brood and checked them for injury. But apart from being dirty and blackened like the rest, they were unharmed. Together once more, they dropped down the side of the house and into the stream of water running off into the gutter.

Down the littered gutter they ran over bits of burned wood, blackened cloth and charred paper, until they reached a large drain like an open mouth at the end of the street.

Then came a period of falling through darkness, of landing with a splash in a foul stream that flowed sluggishly through ill-smelling underground tunnels of brick, dimly lit by occasional gleams from above. Refuse floated on the brackish surface. Huge rats scurried and scrabbled along the side of the brick walls of the sewer.

But in the end there was an emerging towards the open air and the sunlight again, a twist, a turn, a gushing from the sewer mouth and there they were back once more in their broad, beloved river, safe and united.

Yet, it was no longer as it had been before. The hills, the fruitful vineyards and the ancient castles were gone and had been replaced by low pastureland where black and white cows grazed under trees. But Snowflake knew that other changes had taken place as well. They had been through fire. They were all older and wiser, and some of the careless gaiety was gone out of them and their lives.

But the greatest change, Snowflake was sad to see and which filled her with foreboding, had taken place in Raindrop.

The strain of the heroic struggle against the fire had left him altered. His pear-shaped figure was no longer as smooth and robust as it had been and he never seemed to recover his former gay and joyous spirit. He looked worn and older and was apt to have long periods when he was moody and silent.

Yet always he was loving and kind to Snowflake and the children. When his eyes rested upon Snowflake they were filled with such tenderness that her own heart was swelled nearly to bursting. How dear and good he had always been to her.

One morning, as they drifted slowly on the bosom of the broad, placid river passing through flat meadows where many windmills, stirred by the just-awakened breeze, revolved slowly against the pale sky, Snowflake became aware that Raindrop was no longer with her.

The night before he had still been at her side. Now he was gone. With a feeling of sadness that was too deep even for tears, Snowflake knew it was forever.

How could this be? Snowflake asked herself. One moment he had been a part of her, his heartbeat close to hers, the next he had vanished and she was alone.

Why had he been given to her, if only to be taken?

Who had called him away in the night so swiftly that he had not had time even to say "Farewell" . . .?

The questions that tormented her brought back to her thoughts of the mysteries of her childhood and she asked the One who had made her in the long ago: "Was it You who called him? Shall I ever see him again?"

There was no reply but the wind rustling the sails of the windmills. Snowflake cried to herself softly: "How can I bear it without him?"

The children crowded around her to comfort her. They put their arms about her and said: "Don't cry. We will never leave you. . . ."

Snowflake looked at them, smiling through her grief, and wondered. For they were no longer children. They had grown up. Snowdrop and Snowcrystal were like herself, but Rainflake and Raindrop-Minor resembled their father, pear-shaped and full of life and vigour. They were always floating off and getting into mischief, exploring swirl and eddy, splashing against every bit of driftwood, leaf or twig they met in the river.

She comforted herself that they would stay with her as they had promised. Now that Raindrop was gone they were all she had. And to take her mind off grieving for him, she made plans for them.

Snowdrop, who was the most beautiful, might be destined to water a rose in a garden, there to glisten like a diamond on the velvet petal. Snowcrystal loved the gleaming salmon and trout flashing in the depths. She would spend her life with them.

Rainflake, who was adventurous, might some day help to drive a great steam engine. Raindrop-Minor liked to dream. He would be happiest in some placid pond where yellow ducklings swam away the long, lazy summer days.

Thus Snowflake mused as slowly they neared the mouth of the great river.

Time and the river flowed on. The broad stream grew muddy and sluggish as it came to the end of its course through soft meadow and marshland. Clay stirred up from the shallow bottom turned the clear sparkling blue of the waters to dull brown. It was like a soiled and tired traveller after a long trip and Snowflake and her children took on this new colour as well.

Yet, as it is, near to the finish of every journey there was all the stir and excitement of impending arrival *somewhere*, the feeling that everything thereafter would be new and different.

Snowflake was aware of this anticipation in the children. They were eager, restless and impatient and fretful when the river instead of forging onwards dissolved into swirls and eddies and seemed to move in slow circles instead of forward to its destination.

And deep in her heart, Snowflake knew that the time was not far distant when, in spite of the promises they had made, the children must go away and, departing, leave behind with her all the beautiful lives she had dreamed for them. Yet she could not keep from hoping that it would not happen.

At its mouth where it finally entered the sea, the great river divided into five, wandering past the scattered islands of the sunken land.

The main stream drove directly towards the west, pointing like an arrow at the setting sun.

The sun was a red ball on the horizon of the limitless ocean when at last they arrived there.

Pausing only to bid a brief goodbye to Snowflake, each of the children chose a different branch.

Snowdrop turned to the south; Rainflake entered the one that bent south-west. Snowcrystal chose the one leading north; Raindrop-Minor rushed headlong into the arm curving north by west.

Each thought that his or her branch would lead most quickly to adventure and success. They had hardly brushed Snowflake's cheek with the farewell kiss when they were off, quivering with excitement to meet what lay ahead of them. And when each of them reached the bend in the river branch, he or she paused only to turn around and wave a last farewell and then was gone.

Alone, Snowflake took the path to the blood-red west.

In the sea, all was changed from everything Snowflake had ever known.

Its waters were deep, mysterious and restless.

Throughout her life Snowflake had experienced movement, the gay, rapid run of the mountain rill, the frothing charge of the rocky cascade, the airy freedom of the falls, the steady flow of broad rivers and the dance of the wavelets stirred by the summer wind on the surface of the lake.

But the ocean heaved and surged endlessly this way and that, like someone in torment. It rose and fell, swirled and swept, pulsed and rocked as though it could never come to rest. Always the surface appeared moving and troubled, and Snowflake became a part of its aimless procession.

And where before the rivulets and brooks, the streams, the runnels, the torrents, the rivers and the lake of which she had been a part were sweet and fresh, the waters of the vast and boundless ocean were salt, and from then on Snowflake always seemed to have in her mouth the bitter taste of tears.

Everything in the sea was enormous compared with what Snowflake had known in the past, the waves, the currents, the fish and the ships.

When she was called upon to hold up a liner, it

was so huge that one could have packed into it all the boats large and small that Snowflake had ever seen and still have had room for twice as many more.

Where the little lake steamer had been two decks high, these on the ocean had ten or twelve decks, one on top of the other. Where their friend of the paddles and the gay flag had but one thin smokestack, these that plied the seas to and fro had three and four funnels, each one large enough to conceal a house, and the garden too.

And whereas the friendly lake vessel had passed lightly over Snowflake and Raindrop without hurting them, the giant cargo and passenger ships weighing many thousands of tons, crushed her with their great bulk. And besides, now that Raindrop was no longer there to share the burden, the entire weight of these ocean giants fell upon her. Snowflake felt that she was growing tired.

There seemed to be no place that Snowflake could go to find peace in the vast ocean through which she was now drifting aimlessly, driven by wind and current, or roaring storm.

When the weather was bad she tried sinking into the green and gloomy depths where it was always calm and still. But she was frightened there by the monsters that came swimming up to stare with great round eyes as large as dinner plates.

Some had triple rows of jagged teeth, others huge pointed spikes like spears, and once when she sank far into the black deep she encountered fish lighted up as though by electricity. One looked like a railway coach going by at night and another carried two lanterns in front of its hideous face by means of two long spines that shot out from its head. Deeper still there were the white and sightless worms that groped through the dark.

These strange beasts, so unlike the gay, sleek trout and silvery salmon of her beloved rivers and lake, terrified Snowflake and she soon returned to the surface to bear the full brunt of the storms.

The storms too were fearful.

The raging winds whipped the surface of the sea into living mountains of grey waters, their crests white-capped with salt froth racing before the gale.

One moment, Snowflake would be lifted dizzyingly to the top of a watery peak and the next instant she would be plunged to the very bottom of the fluid, heaving valleys of these flying hills to gaze upwards and see them, angry and swollen, looming above her, towering walls of water curving inwards as though about to fall upon her with all their weight and crush her.

At times the wind would snatch her from the topmost mountain crag and send her flying through the air as spray to look down upon the endless marching ranges of the angry sea before she fell back to the surface once more to be buffeted and battered almost beyond endurance.

Sometimes these violent tempests would last for days, driving Snowflake ahead of them for many hundreds of agonising miles before they blew themselves out and came to an end.

Yet, the sea could be calm and friendly too, and there were days when the surface was as still as her lovely lake had been, with the sunshine sparkling on blue waters that were hardly more than ruffled by a delicate wind.

But how vast and lonely it was at those times, and Snowflake thought she almost preferred the menace and excitement of the storm to the empty spaces with not a single thing to see as far as the eye could reach.

Sometimes there might be the masts of ships and the tips of smokestacks to be glimpsed far away below the horizon, or she might be so fortunate as to encounter a single steamer ploughing its way across the empty desert of water, and then Snowflake would try to throw herself in its way just for company, even though the weight of the giant hurt her. But for the most part she appeared to be the centre of a wide and empty circle made by the line where the sea met the sky all about her.

And too, now that Raindrop and the children were gone, there was no one to talk to any more, at least no one that Snowflake cared about, and she learned what it was to be lonely.

One day was just like another in Snowflake's life now—waves, the huge ships with their threshing screws that turned the water to milk behind them, dolphins, porpoises, sharks and whales and other monsters that lurked in the deep. And the trackless sea.

And yet it was not quite the same, for while she did not know where she was going, Snowflake had been driven steadily southwards. The water of which she was a part became warmer, the sun hotter, the seas calmer and the storms less frequent.

Thus she was able to spend more days on the surface under the blue skies, with the burning sun beating down. And gradually Snowflake became aware of a change that was taking place in her. She had felt that for some time she had been growing weaker. The great zest for life and love of living, the pleasure she used to take in all things large and small, was beginning to pass. She was tired much of the time, even when she had been doing nothing but resting and dreaming.

And Snowflake knew that she must be approaching the end of her days.

How this end was to take place, what it would be like, or where she would go, Snowflake could not tell. But she was aware that somehow it would have to do with the sun. She did not understand this and it saddened her, for she remembered how happy she had been the first time she had seen it rise and how she had longed for it through the dark days when she had lain buried beneath the snow on the mountainside.

But the blazing yellow disc had come to be like a furnace glowing in the sky burning with tropical heat and she recalled that other enemy fire, that she had vanquished. She recognised in this blazing star that had once been her friend a force stronger than herself.

At first she resisted, for even though she had lost those dearest to her, she was filled with love of life. Lonely though she was in this vast emptiness, she was still glad to see the colours in the sky at dusk, or watch the yellow moon rise from the rim of the ocean, to greet a bird winging its solitary way across the wastes of water or to try to count the stars that spangled the heavens at night.

But more and more she realised her strength and will were ebbing and that she must soon depart.

Then came the day when the sun beating out of a brazen sky appeared to concentrate its strength and power on her alone. Snowflake knew that she could resist no longer and that her time was come.

And she was frightened.

For she felt that she was being drawn upward from the sea, that the liquid life she had so loved was being drained from her, and that soon she would not be any more.

And in those last moments, her thoughts turned back to the days when she had been young and to the questions that had never been answered. Why? What was the purpose of it all? And above all, Who?

For what reason had she been born, and sent to earth, to be gay, and sad, to have moments of happiness and others of sorrow? To end as nothing, drawn up into the bosom of the sun from the surface of an endless ocean?

Truly, the mystery seemed greater than it ever had before, and more futile. Where was the sense, the rightness, or the beauty in being born but to die, to live but to be wasted in the end?

 Who was the One who had decreed that what had happened to her should happen, and why? Was it only to amuse Himself that He had made her a unique and shining crystal and sent her tumbling from the sky? Or had there been some purpose that she could not guess that lay behind it all?

Had He forgotten her altogether? He had loved her once. She remembered that, and how it felt, warm and sweet, tender and secure as though nothing could ever happen to harm her. Yet how soon He seemed to have tired of her to let her wander and suffer aimlessly through this strange world He had created.

The sea lay below her now. The glowing sun had her in its grip. Already her form was altering from the lovely crystal drop she had occupied for so long. It was shrivelling and drying. Soon there would be nothing left but a tiny feather of vapour adrift in the sky.

High overhead floated a soft white cloud. Was that her destination? Snowflake remembered that it was in a cloud she had been born.

Yet in those last seconds, there were other things that Snowflake remembered too.

She had fallen upon a mountainside and a little girl with a red cap and mittens had passed over her on her sled.

She had been made into the nose of a snowman who resembled a teacher in the village and everyone who had come to see it had laughed and felt the better for it.

She had gone tumbling down the hillside in the spring and had awakened a sleeping violet in a wood.

She had been caught in a mill-race and turned the miller's wheel to grind wheat so that a woman could bake a loaf of bread for her husband and her children.

She had merged with a dear and tender raindrop whom she loved and with him entered a lake where she had spent the happiest days of her life.

As she thought of the lake she remembered all the swimmers she had helped and the bare brown legs of the children she had cooled on hot summer days.

She heard again the gay hoot of the friendly white paddle steamer with the brave flag of red with a white cross at its stern, and she saw the long barges beflagged with wash and merry with music that she had helped to speed safely on their way.

She thought of her children and the contentment of Raindrop on the long journey they had made together.

With a shudder she remembered the awful duel with fire which she had won; she heard again the dying hiss of the vanquished flames and saw once more the figure of the fireman at the window holding the sleeping child in his arms, safe and sound because of her victory.

As she neared the white cloud drifting overhead there came to her in one brief flash of understanding *something* of the vast and beautiful design woven by Him who had created all.

Hers had been a humble life. Never at any time had she been or pretended to be anything but a little snowflake.

But as she looked back she saw that she had been useful, that always when she had been needed she had been there to fulfil her purpose. To have helped a little girl with red cap and red mittens to be in time for school was not to have been born in vain.

Even to have been a part of the nose of a snowman that made people laugh and forget their troubles was useful.

She saw that all her life she had been called upon to serve. She had watered a wild flower, sheltered a frog, speeded a fish, turned the miller's wheel, put out a fire, and held up the bows of the largest liner.

How thoughtful and tender, how exquisitely beautiful, careful and loving was the plan behind all that had happened to her from the very day she was born. And she knew now that never, not for one single, solitary instant, had she been forgotten or overlooked by Him.

For the last time she wondered about the what and why of this world into which she had been born. There had been her mountain, the village, the valley, the river, the lake and the ocean. Each had seemed so huge and yet how small they were when she considered the vast sun, the hanging moon and all the stars in the sky.

As the earth was to the firmament, one tiny wandering sphere, so had she been but one tiny droplet added to the waters that led everywhere to the sea.

There were, then, the great and the small, the beautiful and the ugly, the many and the few, the proud and the humble. Yet she knew now that none was so poor, so tiny, none so humble, unseen or unsung that its role in the Great Design was not as important to Him as that of the most glorious and mighty. The snowflake and the sun were one in significance in the scheme of Creation. A billion interlocking stars were no greater or more loved by Him than the simplest crystal or droplet that fell to earth. There was no one or nothing that did not matter.

And as she thought of the exquisite harmony of the universe in which she had been sent to play her part, peace and contentment came to Snowflake.

Fainter and fainter beat her heart. Soon she would be Snowflake no more, but only a part of the vast, silent spaces of the heavens, a filmy fragment of an autumn cloud.

But in this final moment she experienced once more the warm, tender and all-embracing love that she had felt when first she tumbled from the sky so long ago.

It lulled her with its sweetness, calmed her fears and filled her through and through with joy.

She knew then that the final mystery of Who it was had created her, watched over her and loved her steadfastly as He loved all things both great and small might never be solved for her. It no longer seemed important to her to know, for soon, Whoever or Whatever, she would be a part of Him.

And the last thing she could remember before the sun drew her up into the heart of the cloud above was that all about her the air and the sky seemed to ring with the tender and loving words—"Well done, little Snowflake. Come home to me now."